EARTH SHAPERS

HOW ASTEROIDS SHAPED EARTH

by Jane P. Gardner

pogo

Ideas for Parents and Teachers

Pogo Books let children practice reading informational text while introducing them to nonfiction features such as headings, labels, sidebars, maps, and diagrams, as well as a table of contents, glossary, and index.

Carefully leveled text with a strong photo match offers early fluent readers the support they need to succeed.

Before Reading

- "Walk" through the book and point out the various nonfiction features. Ask the student what purpose each feature serves.
- Look at the glossary together. Read and discuss the words.

Read the Book

- Have the child read the book independently.
- Invite him or her to list questions that arise from reading.

After Reading

- Discuss the child's questions. Talk about how he or she might find answers to those questions.
- Prompt the child to think more. Ask: An asteroid wiped out the dinosaurs and changed Earth to what it is today. Can you imagine what it would be like to live with dinosaurs?

Pogo Books are published by Jump!
5357 Penn Avenue South
Minneapolis, MN 55419
www.jumplibrary.com

Library of Congress Cataloging-in-Publication Data

Names: Gardner, Jane P., author.
Title: How asteroids shaped Earth / by Jane P. Gardner.
Description: Minneapolis, MN: Jump!, Inc., [2021]
Series: Earth shapers | Includes index. | Audience: Age 7-10.
Identifiers: LCCN 2019019008 (print)
LCCN 2019021894 (ebook)
ISBN 9781645271178 (hardcover: alk. paper)
ISBN 9781645271185 (pbk.)
ISBN 9781645271192 (ebook)
Subjects: LCSH: Asteroids–Juvenile literature.
Classification: LCC QB651 .G37 2021 (print)
LCC QB651 (ebook) | DDC 551.3/97–dc23
LC record available at https://lccn.loc.gov/2019019008
LC ebook record available at https://lccn.loc.gov/2019021894

Editor: Jenna Gleisner
Designer: Michelle Sonnek

Photo Credits: Kyodo News/Getty, cover; Dotted Yeti/Shutterstock, 1 (top), 23; max dallocoo/Shutterstock, 1 (bottom); fretschi/Shutterstock, 3; Savoul Pelister/Shutterstock, 4; Mopic/Shutterstock, 5; Alexyz3d/Shutterstock, 6-7; Mode-list/iStock, 8-9; Viktar Malyshchyts/Shutterstock, 10-11; Take 27 Ltd/Science Source, 12; lHelly/Shutterstock, 13 (top); MarcelClemens/Shutterstock, 13 (middle); Bjoern Wylezivh/Shutterstock, 13 (bottom); Detlev van Ravenswaay/Science Source, 14-15; Wirestock Images/Shutterstock, 16-17; leungchopan/Shutterstock, 18 (woman); NASA, 18 (screen); Science History Images/Alamy, 19; Martina Badini/Shutterstock, 20-21.

Printed in the United States of America at Corporate Graphics in North Mankato, Minnesota.

TABLE OF CONTENTS

CHAPTER 1

CRASHING INTO EARTH

Dinosaurs once ruled Earth. Then about 66 million years ago, a giant **impact** changed our planet. What happened?

A huge **asteroid** hit Earth! Tons of dust filled the **atmosphere**. It blocked the sun! Earth was dark for several years.

The planet cooled. Many plants and animals died. This included the dinosaurs. Earth would not warm again for decades.

Asteroids are rocky objects in space. They can be as small as pebbles. Others are more than 300 miles (483 kilometers) across!

DID YOU KNOW?

How big was the asteroid that killed the dinosaurs? Scientists think it was about six miles (9.7 km) across. Its impact caused huge **earthquakes**. It caused **tsunamis**, too. Wildfires started. They burned for months.

asteroid

Asteroids **orbit** the sun. Most are in the asteroid belt. They formed around the same time as the planets. This was about 4.6 billion years ago!

TAKE A LOOK!

Take a look at our **solar system**. See the asteroid belt.
Which planets are closest to it?

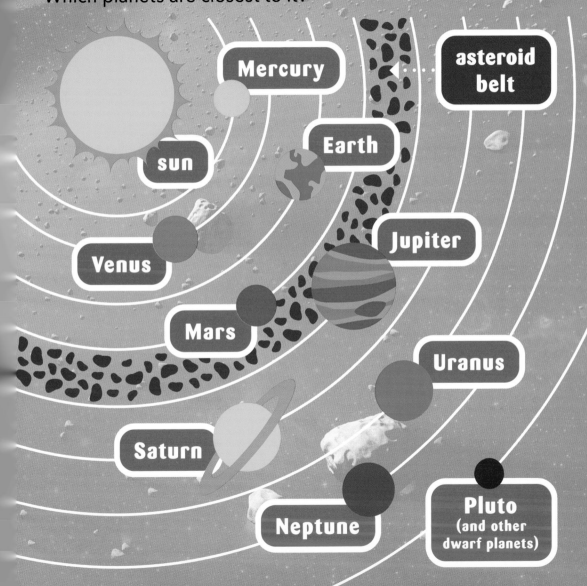

meteor

Asteroids can hit each other in orbit. Pieces break off. They become **meteoroids**. Many of these pass through Earth's atmosphere. These are **meteors**. Most burn up, and we call them shooting stars. Some meteors reach Earth's surface. These are **meteorites**.

DID YOU KNOW?

Sometimes many meteoroids hit Earth's atmosphere. Why? Earth moves into their paths as it orbits. We call this a meteor shower!

CHAPTER 2

SHAPING EARTH

Some scientists think asteroids formed our planet. How? **Gravity** pulled many large ones together.

Each one brought space materials to Earth. These include clay, iron, and gold!

clay

iron

gold

Chicxulub crater

Mexico

After Earth formed, asteroid impacts made **craters**. The asteroid that killed the dinosaurs made a large crater. You can see it from space! Part of it is underwater. It is called the Chicxulub crater. It is in Mexico.

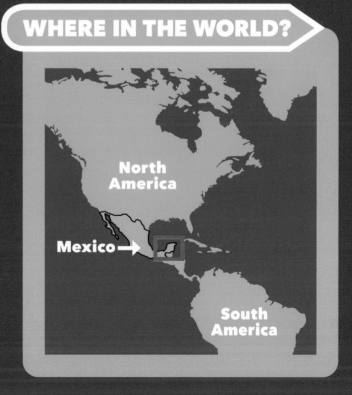

WHERE IN THE WORLD?

North America

Mexico →

South America

This asteroid shaped life on Earth, too. Many ocean animals died. The dinosaurs did, too. But other land animals **thrived**. Why? Dinosaurs were not there to hunt them. The plants dinosaurs would have eaten were now available to eat. Slowly, life became what we know today.

CHAPTER 3

TRACKING AND USING ASTEROIDS

Earth crosses paths with space objects each day. Some are asteroids! Scientists track their paths. Why? They work to keep Earth safe.

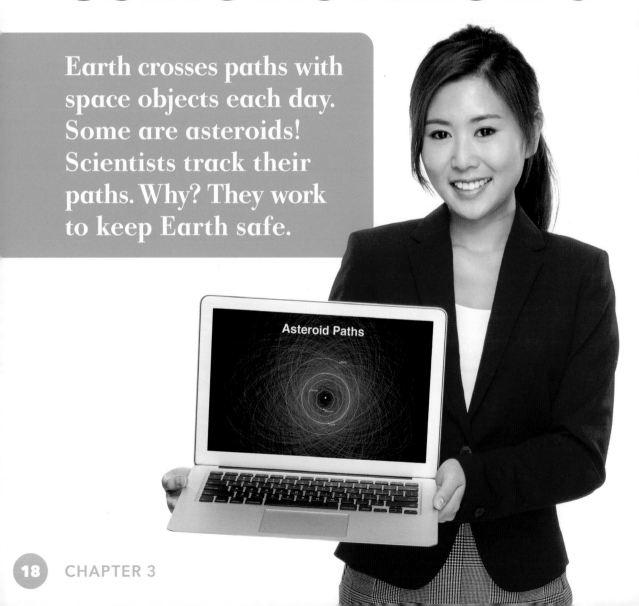

Asteroid Paths

Asteroids can be helpful. They have useful things, like water, iron, and clay. In the future, we may be able to use these. Scientists are looking for ways.

Asteroids may have formed our planet. Life on Earth is different because of them.

Large asteroid collisions don't happen often. But they make a big impact!

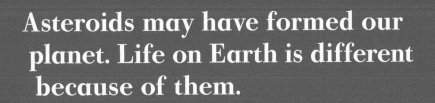

DID YOU KNOW?

Some asteroids have water on them. This could help **astronauts**. How? They could use the water in space. They could then take trips farther into space.

ACTIVITIES & TOOLS

CREATE CRATERS

Asteroids leave craters. The size and shape of the crater tells a lot about the asteroid.

What You Need:
- newspaper
- large plastic tub
- flour
- marbles of different sizes

❶ Cover a surface with newspaper. Set the plastic tub in the center of the newspaper.

❷ Pour flour into the tub until it is two inches (5 centimeters) deep. Gently shake the tub to level out the flour.

❸ Stand above the tub and drop a marble into the flour. Remove the marble and observe the crater.

❹ Shake the tub to make a smooth surface again.

❺ Try again. Use different-sized marbles. Or drop them from different heights. How do the crater sizes change?

GLOSSARY

asteroid: A rocky object that travels around the sun.

astronauts: People who are trained to travel in space.

atmosphere: The mixture of gases that surrounds a planet.

craters: Hollows or depressions in Earth's crust.

earthquakes: Sudden shakings of the ground.

gravity: The force that pulls things toward the center of Earth and keeps them from floating away.

impact: When two things collide.

meteorites: Pieces of rock from space that fall to Earth.

meteoroids: Small pieces of asteroids in space.

meteors: Pieces of rock or metal from space that speed into Earth's atmosphere and form streaks of light as they burn and fall to Earth.

orbit: To travel in a circular path around something, especially a planet or the sun.

solar system: The sun together with the planets, many moons, asteroids, and comets that move in orbit around it.

thrived: Became successful or healthy and strong.

tsunamis: Very large, destructive waves caused by underwater earthquakes or volcanoes.

INDEX

TO LEARN MORE

Finding more information is as easy as 1, 2, 3.

❶ **Go to www.factsurfer.com**

❷ **Enter "howasteroidsshapedEarth" into the search box.**

❸ **Choose your book to see a list of websites.**

FACT SURFER